A KEYBOARD ANTHOLOGY · FIRST SERIES
Edited by Howard Ferguson

BOOK II

GW00646805

1
THE FALL OF THE LEAFE

MARTIN PEERSON

Source: the *Fitzwilliam Virginal Book*, a large anthology of keyboard music, copied by Francis Tregian the younger during his confinement in the Fleet Prison (1609–19) on the charge of recusancy. Twenty-four ornaments have been omitted. All phrase-marks and dynamics are editorial. H.F.

2
CORRENTE in A minor

FRESCOBALDI

Source: Frescobaldi's *Toccate d'intavoltura di cimbalo et organo*, 1637. All phrase-marks and dynamics are editorial. H.F.

A.B.1700

3
VIVACE in A

RATHGEBER

Source: *Musikalischer Zeit-Vertreib auf dem Klavier*, 1743. All phrase-marks and dynamics are editorial. H.F.

4
L'INDIFFÉRENTE

RAMEAU

(a) original sign: ... = ... (b) original sign: ... = ...

Source: *Nouvelles Suites de Pièces de clavecin*, [c. 1728]. Twenty-four of the original ornaments have been omitted and modern signs substituted for those used by Rameau (see footnotes). All phrase-marks are editorial. In accordance with the 18th-century French convention of *notes inégales*, a slight lilt should be given to the rhythm by fractionally lengthening the first note in each pair of quavers and shortening the second – very approximately ... . H.F.

(c) original signs:

5
SONATINA in B flat

HANDEL, B. 60/27

This isolated movement is taken from the Third Collection of *Suites de Pièces pour le Clavecin;* G. F. Witvogel, Amsterdam 1733. The original contains no phrasing or dynamics. H.F.

A.B.1700

6
PRELUDE in C minor

BACH, BWV 999

Originally intended for the lute, this isolated prelude comes from a manuscript which belonged to Bach's young contemporary admirer, Johann Peter Kellner. The original contained neither dynamics nor phrase-marks; but the performer on either lute or clavichord would have allowed his own dynamics to echo the melodic rise and fall or the harmonic tension and relaxation of the music, as suggested by the present editorial markings. H.F.

A.B.1700

7
SONATA in G

Allegro [♩ = c.126]

SCARLATTI, K.391, L.79

Source: the text is taken from one of the fifteen manuscript volumes of keyboard works now belonging to the Biblioteca Palatina, Parma. The two-note slurs in bars 1, 2, 5, 6 and 41–3 are in the original. The remaining phrase-marks and all dynamics are editorial. H.F.

8
SONATA in A
Third movement

GALUPPI

Source: a manuscript in the Istituto Venturi, Brescia. All phrase-marks and dynamics are editorial. H.F.

A.B.1700

A.B.1700

9
SONATA in A flat
Second movement

HAYDN, Hob. XVI/43

The text is based on the first edition, published by Beardmore & Birchall, London 1783, which contains few phrase-marks and dynamics. H.F.

10
ANDANTINO in E flat

MOZART, K. 236

The history of this isolated *Andantino* is obscure; but it may have been written in 1790 for an autograph album of J. B. Cramer which no longer exists. The first edition of 1852, which provides the present text, contains no dynamic marks. H.F.

11
PASTORALE

JAMES HOOK, Op. 25

Source: Divertimento No. 8 from *A third set of twelve Divertimentos for the harpsichord or piano-forte*, Op.25; T. Skillern, London [1782].
The tempo-mark and all phrase-marks and dynamics are editorial, as there are none in the original. H.F.

12
TWO MOVEMENTS OF A SONATINA

BEETHOVEN, WoO 50

These two movements were written by the 18-year-old Beethoven in Bonn for his friend, Franz Gerhard Wegeler. All phrase-marks and dynamics are editorial. H.F.

Allegretto [♩ = c.120]

13
ERSTER VERLUST
(First Loss)

SCHUMANN, Op. 68, No. 16

Nicht schnell
[**Moderato** ♩ = 72]

Source: Schumann's autograph of *Album für die Jugend*, Op.68, written in 1848. Marks within square brackets have been added by the editor. H.F.

A.B.1700

14
CHANT DE LA CREUSE
(Song from the Creuse)

FRANCK

Très lent [♩ = c. 52]

Source: *L'Organiste: 44 Petites Pièces;* Enoch, Paris [n.d.].

A.B.1700

15
STUDY in A flat

HELLER, Op. 47, No. 23

Source: *Studies*, Op.47, Book 3.

16
WATCHMAN'S SONG

GRIEG, Op. 12, No. 3

Molto andante e semplice [♩ = c. 96]

Intermezzo *(Spirits of the night)*

Source: *Lyrische Stückchen*, Book 1, Op. 12₁; Peters, Leipzig.

A.B.1700

17
CHANSON RUSSE
(Russian Song)

GLIÈRE, Op. 34, No. 15

Source: *24 Pièces caractéristiques pour la jeunesse*, Op.34; P. Jurgenson, Leipzig & Moscow 1908.

18
PRIÈRE DU MATIN
(Morning Prayer)

TCHAIKOVSKY, Op. 39, No.1

Source: *Jugend Album*, Op.39; Jurgenson, Moscow 1893.

A.B.1700

Printed in England by Caligraving Limited Thetford Norfolk

2:05